THE BEST

the Waterboys

'81-'90

*All the tracks from
the album arranged for voice,
piano and guitar.*

Wise Publications
London / New York / Sydney

6.95

Exclusive Distributors:

Music Sales Limited
8/9 Frith Street,
London W1V 5TZ, England.

Music Sales Pty Limited
120 Rothschild Avenue, Rosebery,
NSW 2018, Australia.

This book © Copyright 1991 by
Wise Publications
Order No. AM86280
ISBN 0.7119.2772.3

Book design by Michael Bell Design.
Music arranged by Pat Fitzpatrick and Roger Day.
Music processed by Musicprint.
Typeset by Capital Setters.

Music Sales' complete catalogue
lists thousands of titles and is free
from your local music shop, or direct from
Music Sales Limited.
Please send a cheque/postal order
for £1.50 for postage to:
Music Sales Limited,
Newmarket Road, Bury St. Edmunds,
Suffolk IP33 3YB.

Printed in the United Kingdom by
Caligraving Limited, Thetford, Norfolk.

A Girl called Johnny

Words & Music by Mike Scott

D9

Dm7   Fmaj7

Am

(1.)   I ____ re - mem - ber John - ny   hey, ___
(2.)   I ____   re - mem - ber a   girl ____ called John - ny,
(%) *See block lyric*

Am/G

____ black as hell, ___   John - ny come   late - ly ___
white as   a   ghost. ___

10

dis - cov-ered her ___ choice was to change ___
they would have torn ___ her to piec - es but

or to be ___ changed. ___
who would dare. ___

(Solo)

13

VERSE 3: (D.S.)
I remember a girl called Johnny
The train came to town
Boy! She got on it
Without looking back
With barely a word if she
Said goodbye, well I never heard
But the noise goes on
The noise! The jazz!
And the truth is in somebody else's hands
And the house that
A girl called Johnny built
Is now just so much
Ashes and sand.

The Big Music

Words & Music by Mike Scott

18

All the Things she gave Me

Words & Music by Mike Scott

All the things ___

all the things she gave ___ me. All the things ___

all the things she gave ___ me.

(1.) I wrapped them up ___ in a big brown box ___
dark as hell in here, the ci-ty's grown cold, ___ the

tied it with. rib - bon, drove ___ to the docks.
de - vil's in drag, playing po - ker with souls. The

checked my time ___ by the old town clock, ___ all the
lots are all emp - ty. The last man's out, ___ the

things.
moon's made of cheese ___ and God is a boy ___ scout, when

watch-man
I go to sleep, ___ I'll be dream-ing a-bout ___ all the

things.
cupped hands ___ as he walked ___ to the car. ___ He said
Then I'll

"Where d'you think you're driv - ing to son? ___ All good
dream a-bout chur-ches with great tall spires, ___ All good cath-

folks are in bed ___ and the day's work is done." ___ I said
-e - drals and can - dles, and chim - neys and choirs. ___ And I'll

"I'm just look - ing for some - place to burn." ___ All the
dream a - bout that ___ place where ___ I set fire. ___ All the

things, all the things that she, all the things that she gave ___

___ me, where do I put ___ them, where {do}{must} I hide ___ them?

22

All the things that she gave ____ me, where do I put ____ ____ them { I don't / where I can } have to see them.

(2.) It's keep them a - way out of my

life.

All the things she gave ___ me.

All the things, ___

all the things she gave ___ me.

Ad lib to Fade

All the things ___

The Whole of the Moon

Words & Music by Mike Scott

you saw the plan.
you cut through ties.

I wan - dered out in the world for years
I saw the rain dirt - y val - ley,

while you just stayed in your room, I saw the
you just saw Bri - ga - doon, I saw the

cres - cent,
cres - cent,

you saw the whole of the
you saw the whole of the

1.

moon,

the whole of the moon.

you just knew, ___ I sighed,   but

you   swooned,   I ___ saw   the cres - cent,

you saw   the whole of   the moon,

the whole of   the moon.

D.%. al Coda

With a

29

wind in your sails, you came like a co-met, blaz-ing your trail.

Too high, too far, too soon,

Repeat ad lib.

you saw the whole of the (moon.)

Spirit

Words & Music by Mike Scott

man sur - ren - ders,
man dreams,

spi - rit won't,
the spi - rit lives,

man is crawls,
man is teth - ered,

spi - rit flies,
spi - rit free,

spi - rit lives   when   man   dies, ___   be.
what spi - rit is   man   can ___

(2.) Man ___

What spi - rit is   man   can ___   be,

Ad lib to Fade

what spi - rit is

Don't Bang the Drum

Words & Music by Mike Scott & Karl Wallinger

Now we stand _____ in a spe-cial place _____ what _____ will you do here? What show of soul _____ are we gon-na get from you? It could be de-li-ve-rance or his-to-ry un-der these skies so blue, _____

could be some-thing true, ___ but if I ___

know you ___ you'll bang ___ the drum ___ like mon-keys do. ___

1.

(2.) Well here we are ___

2.

Here we stand ___ on a

VERSE 2:
Here we are in a fabulous place
What are you gonna dream here?
We are standin' in this fabulous place
What are you gonna play here?
I know you love the high life
You love to leap around,
You love to beat your chest
And make your sound,
But not here man!
This is sacred ground
With a power flowing through
And if I know you you'll
Bang the drum like monkeys do.

40

Fisherman's Blues

Words & Music by Mike Scott & Steve Wickham

Cast-ing out my sweet ___ line with a - ban-don- ment ___ and love.

No ceil -ing bear -ing down on me, save the

star - ry sky ___ a - bove ___ with light ___ in my head

and you ___ in my arms.

VERSE 2:
I wish I was the brakeman
On a hurtling, fevered train
Rushing headlong into the heartland
Like a cannon in the rain
With the beating of the sleepers
And the burning of the coal
Counting the towns flashing by
In a night that's full of soul
With light in my head
And you in my arms.

VERSE 3:
I know I will be loosened
From the bonds that hold me fast
That the chains all hung around me
Will fall away at last
And on that fine and fateful day
I will take me in my hands
I will ride on the train
I will be the fisherman
With light in my head
And you in my arms.

Killing My Heart

Words & Music by Mike Scott

morn-ing time if I know you.   You ain't

call-in' me to join you and I'm spo-ken for an-y-way.

But you'll be kill-ing my heart

when you go _ a-way.   (2.) Shall we

VERSE 2:
Shall we gather by the river
For to hear the lovely thunder crash
Will you sail now in your speeding bonnie boat
Here and gone like a splash
You will see me small, receding, mouth hung open
Words I can not say
You'll be killing my heart
When you go away.

VERSE 3:
Mike Rogers left his whisky
And the night is very, very young
There's much to tell and more to say
The words will soon be spilling from my tongue
I will rave and I will ramble I'll do everything
But make you stay
But you'll be killing my heart
When you go away.

Strange Boat

Words & Music by Mike Scott & Anthony Thistlethwaite

Gently

We're sail - ing in a strange boat, ___ head - ing for a
strange sea, ___ blown by a
strange time, ___ work - ing for a

strange shore,— we're sail-ing in a strange boat,—
strange wind,— we're sail-ing on a strange sea,—
strange goal,— we're liv-ing in a strange time,—

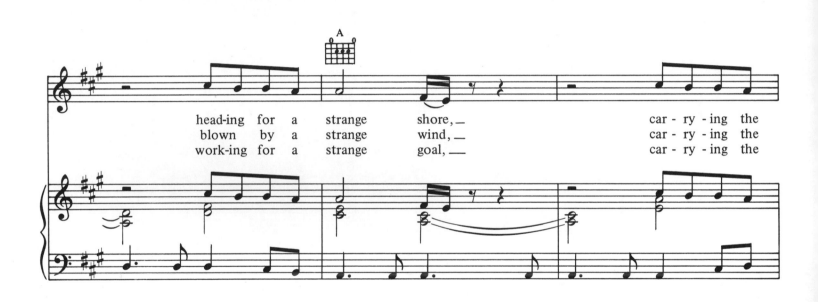

head-ing for a strange shore,— car-ry-ing the
blown by a strange wind,— car-ry-ing the
work-ing for a strange goal,— car-ry-ing the

strang-est car-go that was e-ver hauled a-board.—
strang-est crew— that e-ver sinned.—
we're turn-ing flesh and body in-to soul.—

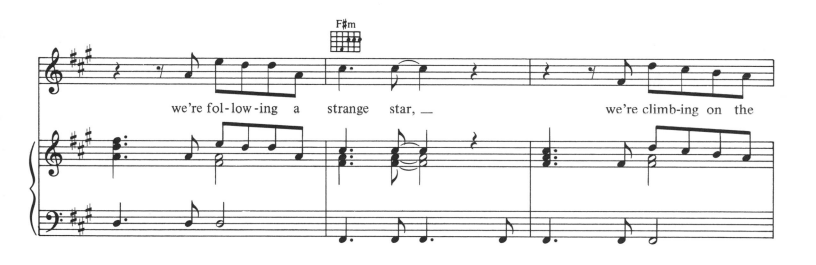

And a Bang on the Ear

Words & Music by Mike Scott

Lind - say was my

51

first love, she was in my class.

I would have loved to take her out—

— but I was too shy to ask.

The full - ness of my

feel -ing was ne - ver made clear.

(𝄋 Vocal)

but I send her my

love and a bang on the ear.

1-7.   8.   D.S. (Instr.)
              al Coda

⊕ CODA   G

ear.   I'll

53

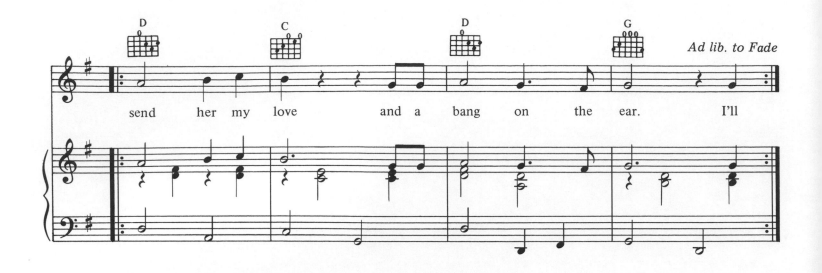

send her my love and a bang on the ear. I'll

VERSE 2:

Nora was my girl when I first was in a group
I can still see her to this day stirring chicken soup
Now she's living in Australia working for an auctioneer
I send her my love and a bang on the ear.

VERSE 3:

Deborah broke my heart and I the willing fool
I fell for her one summer on the road to Liverpool
I thought it was forever but it was over within the year
I send her my love and a bang on the ear.

VERSE 4: (Instrumental)

VERSE 5:

The home I made with Bella became a house of pain
We weathered it together bound by a ball and chain
It started up in Fife; it ended up in tears
I send her my love and a bang on the ear.

VERSE 6:

Krista was a rover, from Canada she hailed
We crossed swords in San Francisco; we both lived to tell the tale
I don't know now where she is, oh but if I had her here
I'd give her my love and a bang on the ear.

VERSE 7: (Instrumental)

VERSE 8:

So my woman of the hearthfire, harbour of my soul
I watch you lightly sleeping, I sense the dream that does unfold, like gold,
You to me are treasure, you to me are dear
So I'll give you my love and a bang on the ear.

VERSE 9: (D.S.) (Instrumental)
. . . . I'll give you my love and a bang on the ear.

Old England

Words & Music by Mike Scott

(1.) Man looks up ___ on a yel-low sky ___ and the rain turns to rust in his eye.

Ru-mours of his health are lies

old Eng-land is dy - ing.

(Solo)

dy -ing.

VERSES:

2. His clothes are a dirty shade of blue
And his ancient shoes worn through
He steals from me and he lies to you
Old England is dying.

3. Still he sings an Empire song
Still he keeps his navy strong
And he sticks his flag where it ill belongs
Old England is dying.

LYRICS AT **B**

I just freeze in the wind and I'm
Numb from the pummelin' of the snow
That falls from high in yellow skies
Where the time stained flag of England flies
Where the homes are warm and mothers sigh.
Where comedians laugh and babies cry
Where criminals are televised, politicians fraternize
Journalists are dignified and everyone is civilised.

A Man is in Love

Words & Music by Mike Scott
(Incorporating Caliope House. Music by Dave Richardson)

man is in love _____ with you _____

VERSE 2:
A man is in love
How did I hear?
I heard him talk too much
Whenever you're near
He whispered your name
When his eyes were closed
A man is in love
And he knows.

VERSE 3: (Instrumental)

VERSE 4:
A man is in love
How did I guess?
I figured it out while he was
Watching you dress
He'd give you his all
If you'd but agree
A man is in love
And he's me.